P9-AGD-091

"Flowers"

The National Gallery Address Book

Designed and illustrations selected by Sally McIntosh
National Gallery Design Studio

Cover illustration
Jan van Huysum 1682–1749
(detail) *Hollyhocks and other Flowers in a Vase*

Half title
Ascribed to the **Master of the Cassoni**
(detail) *Birth Plate: The Triumph of Love (reverse)*

Frontispiece
Ascribed to **Pierre Andrieu** 1821–1892
(detail) *Still life with Fruit and Flowers*

Reprinted 1989
Published by order of the Trustees
ISBN 0 947645 54 3

Printed in the UK by Jolly & Barber Limited, Rugby

Colour origination by P J Graphics

In 1824 the British Government took the decision to found a National Gallery with the nucleus of thirty-eight paintings, based on the collection of the Russian emigré banker, John Julius Angerstein. It was a small but choice collection, gathered with the aid of Sir Thomas Lawrence, and included major paintings by Raphael, Claude Lorraine and Hogarth. The Government would perhaps not have taken such a step, had it not already been promised the collection of Sir George Beaumont, which included paintings by Rubens and Canaletto.

In 1824 the National Gallery opened at 100 Pall Mall, Angerstein's town house. This quickly became too small and in 1838 the National Gallery moved into its present building, designed by William Wilkins.

The collection continued to grow rapidly and by the end of the 19th century included over 1,000 paintings. Today the Collection numbers well over 2,000 paintings, representing masterpieces of European painting from the 13th to the early 20th century.

All Sorts of Flowers

Fresh spring the herald of loves mighty king,
  In whose cote armour richly are displayd
  all sorts of flowers the which on earth do spring
  in goodly colours gloriously arrayd.
Goe to my love, where she is careless layd,
  yet in her winters bowre not well awake:
  tell her the joyous time will not be staid
  unless she does him by the forelock take.
Bid her therefore her selfe soone ready make,
  to wayt on love amongst his lovely crew:
  where every one that misseth then her make,
  shall be by him amearst with penance dew.
Make hast therefore sweet love, whilest it is prime,
  for none can call againe the passed time.

from *Amoretti Verse VII* by Edmund Spenser (?1552–1599)

Paulus Theodorus van Brussel 1754–1795
(detail) *Flowers in a Vase*

A

ADDRESS

TELEPHONE

ADDRESS	TELEPHONE

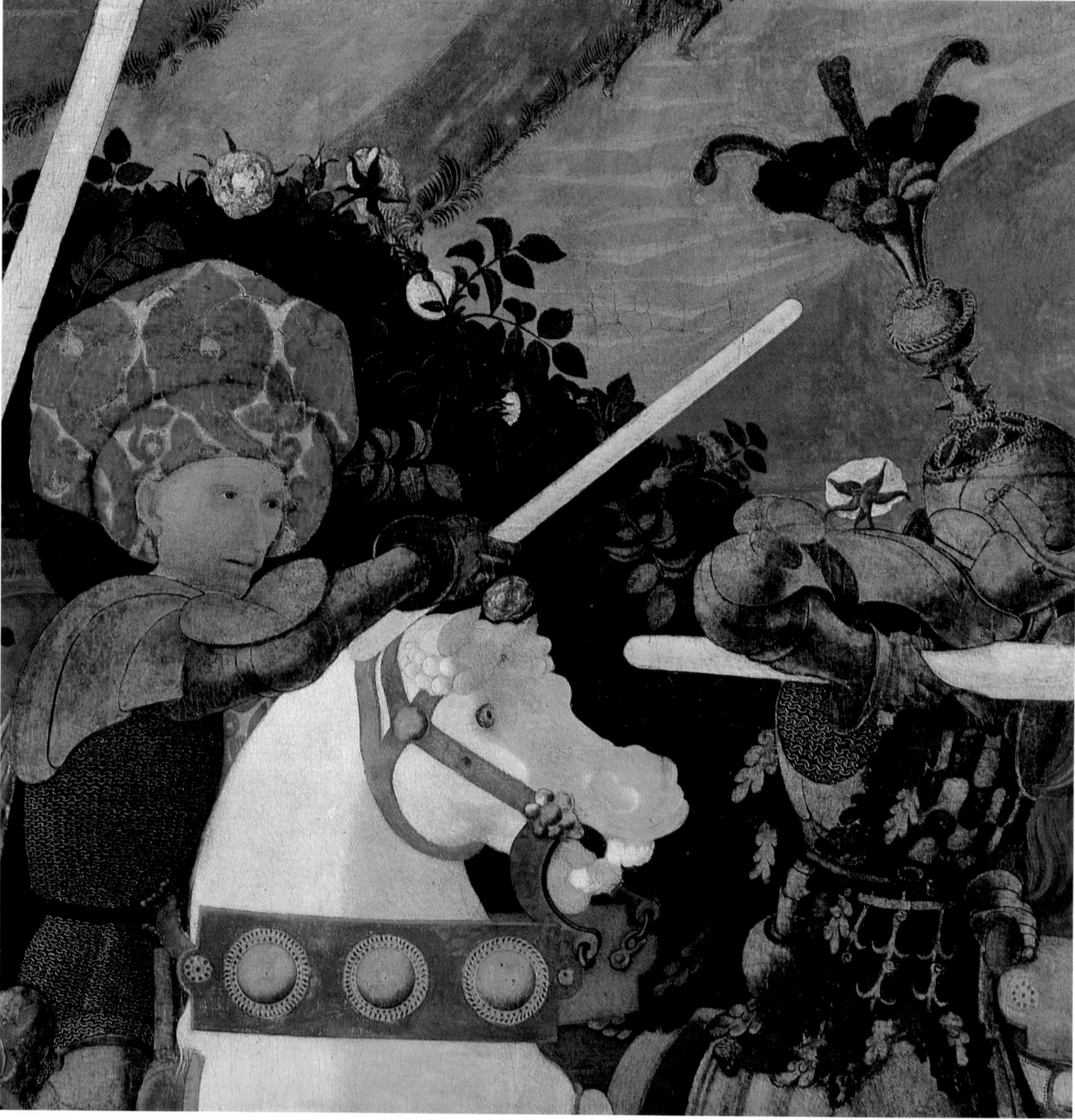

Paolo Uccello c.1397–1475
(detail) *The Battle of San Romano*

ADDRESS	TELEPHONE

B

ADDRESS

TELEPHONE

ADDRESS

TELEPHONE

Following pages
Odilon Redon 1840–1916
(detail) *Ophelia among the Flowers*

B

ADDRESS

TELEPHONE

ADDRESS	TELEPHONE

Master of Saint Giles active c.1500
(detail) *Saint Giles and the Hind*

ADDRESS

TELEPHONE

C

ADDRESS	TELEPHONE

ADDRESS	TELEPHONE

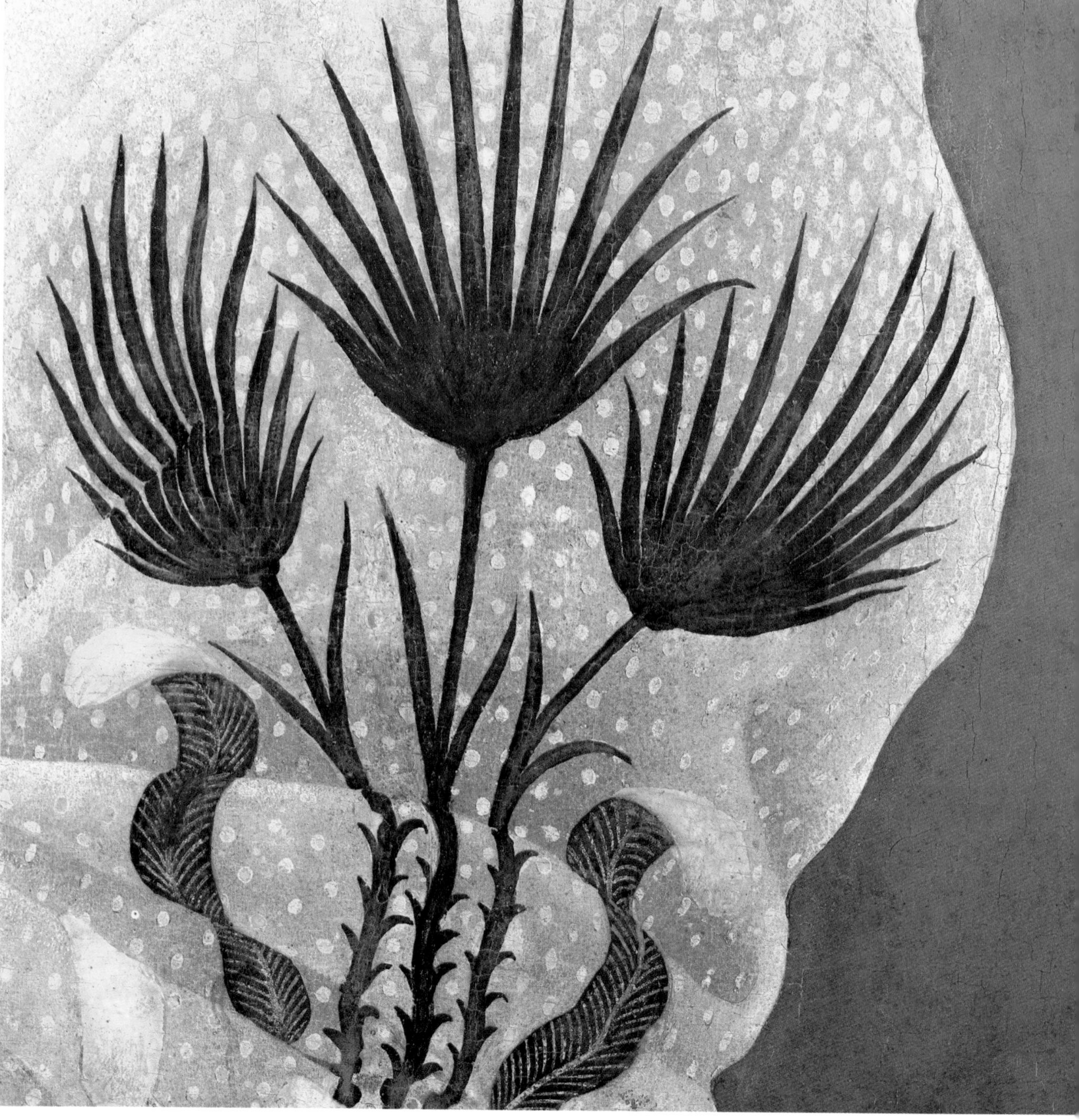

Alesso Baldovinetti c.1426–1499
(detail) *Portrait of a Lady in Yellow*

D

ADDRESS

TELEPHONE

D

ADDRESS	TELEPHONE

ADDRESS

TELEPHONE

Following pages, from left
Giovanni Battista Tiepolo 1696–1770
(detail) *A Seated Man, a Woman with a Jar, and a Boy*

Jean-Marc Nattier 1685–1766
(detail) *Manon Balletti*

ADDRESS	TELEPHONE

ADDRESS	TELEPHONE

Claude-Oscar Monet 1840–192
(detail) *Iris*

ADDRESS

TELEPHONE

F

ADDRESS	TELEPHONE

ADDRESS	TELEPHONE

Bronzino 1503–15

(detail) *An Allego*

ADDRESS

TELEPHONE

H

ADDRESS	TELEPHONE

ADDRESS

TELEPHONE

Following pages
Vincent van Gogh 1853–1890
(detail) *Long Grass with Butterflies*

H

ADDRESS

TELEPHONE

ADDRESS

TELEPHONE

Fantin-Latour 1836–1904
(detail) '*The Rosy Wealth of June*

ADDRESS

TELEPHONE

J

ADDRESS

TELEPHONE

ADDRESS	TELEPHONE

Jean-Desire-Gustave Courbet 1819–187
(detail) *The Girls of the Seine Bank*

ADDRESS

TELEPHONE

L

ADDRESS	TELEPHONE

L

ADDRESS

TELEPHONE

ADDRESS	TELEPHONE

M

ADDRESS

TELEPHONE

ADDRESS

TELEPHONE

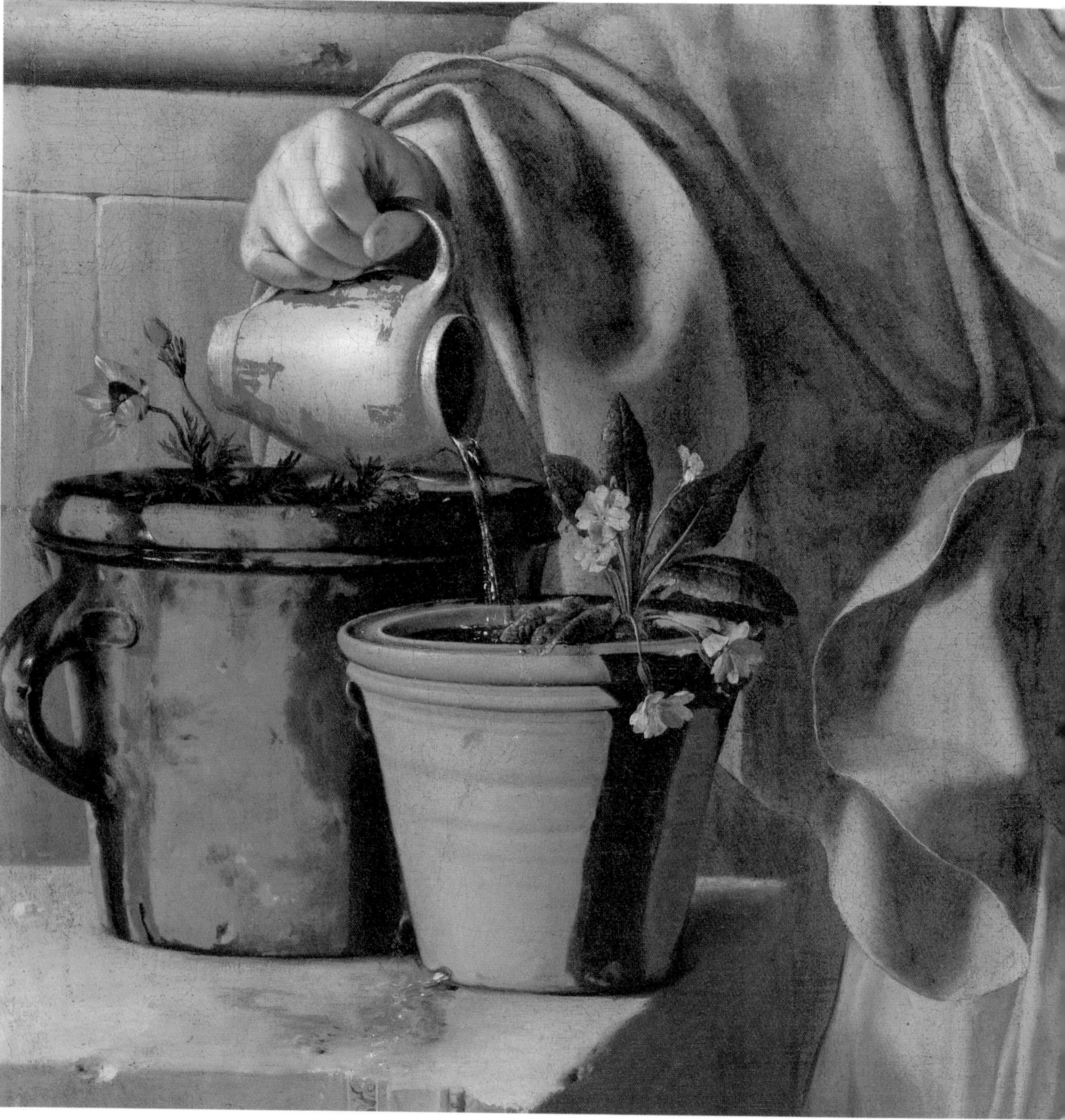

aurent de La Hire 1606–1656
letail) *Allegorical Figure of Grammar*

M

ADDRESS

TELEPHONE

Mc

ADDRESS

TELEPHONE

ADDRESS	TELEPHONE

Following pages
Paul Gauguin 1848–1903
(detail) *A Vase of Flowers*

N

ADDRESS	TELEPHONE

ADDRESS	TELEPHONE

Jean-Honore Fragonard 1732–180
(detail) *Psyche showing her Sisters her Gifts from Cupi*

ADDRESS

TELEPHONE

P

ADDRESS	TELEPHONE

ADDRESS	TELEPHONE

Nicolas Lancret 1690–1743
(detail) *A Lady and Gentleman with two Girls in a Garden ('La Tasse de Chocolat')*

ADDRESS	TELEPHONE

P

ADDRESS	TELEPHONE

ADDRESS

TELEPHONE

Following pages, from left

Rachel Ruysch 1664–1750
(detail) *Flowers in a Vase*

Jean-Auguste-Dominique Ingres 1780–1867
(detail) *Madame Moitessier Seated*

R

ADDRESS

TELEPHONE

ADDRESS	TELEPHONE

Fra Filippo Lippi c.1406(?)–146
(detail) *The Annunciatio*

ADDRESS

TELEPHONE

S

ADDRESS

TELEPHONE

ADDRESS

TELEPHONE

ollower of **Quinten Massys** 1465/6–1530
letail) *Saint Luke painting the Virgin and Child*

S

ADDRESS

TELEPHONE

S

ADDRESS

TELEPHONE

ADDRESS

TELEPHONE

Following pages
French(?) School
(detail) '*The Wilton Diptych*'

T

ADDRESS

TELEPHONE

ADDRESS	TELEPHONE

Rembrandt 1606–1669
(detail) *Saskia van Ulenborch*

ADDRESS

TELEPHONE

V

ADDRESS	TELEPHONE

ADDRESS

TELEPHONE

ADDRESS	TELEPHONE

XYZ

ADDRESS	TELEPHONE

VISITORS' INFORMATION

Raphael 1483–1[illegible]
(detail) *An Allegory ('Vision of a Knigh*

The National Gallery
Trafalgar Square
London WC2N 5DN

Admission Free
Telephone 01-839 3321
Recorded Information 01-839 3526

Open
Monday to Saturday 10.00 am to 6.00 pm
Sunday 2.00 pm to 6.00 pm
Closed on New Year's Day, Good Friday, May Day, Christmas Eve, Christmas Day.

Disabled visitors should come in at the Orange Street entrance where ramps leading to the Gallery are situated, as well as lifts to all floors and toilets. Wheelchairs are available on request.

Daily Events
Guided tours and lunchtime lectures

National Gallery Shop
Open Monday to Saturday 10.00 am to 5.40 pm
Sunday 2.00 pm to 5.40 pm

National Gallery Restaurant
Open Monday to Saturday 10.00 am to 5.00 pm
Sunday 2.00 pm to 5.00 pm

Underground Stations
Charing Cross, Embankment, Leicester Square, Piccadilly Circus

British Rail
Charing Cross

Buses
1, 1a, 3, 6, 9, 11, 12, 13, 15, 15a, 24, 29, 53, 77, 77a, 88, 159, 170, 176, 199

Car Parks
National Car Park in St. Martin's Street

Following pag
Piero di Cosim
(detail) *A Mythological Subjec*